Data Analysis

5–6

Written by

Pamela Jennett and Steve Davis

Editors: Carla Hamaguchi and Jennifer Busby
Illustrator: Corbin Hillam
Production: Carrie Rickmond
Cover Designer: Barbara Peterson
Art Director: Moonhee Pak
Project Manager: Collene Dobelmann
Project Director: Betsy Morris

Table of Contents

Introduction

Data Analysis 5–6 contains ready-to-use activity pages to provide your students with skill practice. The activities can be used to supplement and enhance what your students are already learning at school. Give an activity page to students as independent class work, or send the pages home as homework to reinforce skills taught in class. An answer key is included at the end of the book as a convenient reference.

This book provides activities that will directly assist students in practicing basic skills and concepts. The structure of the book enhances their learning and enables them to meet new challenges with confidence. Students will receive reinforcement in the following skills:

- recognize terminology related to data collection and statistics
- collect and display data using tables and graphs
- interpret information presented in tables and graphs
- analyze information found in different types of graphs
- create tables and graphs from given information
- understand and calculate averages, mean, median, mode, and range

Use *Data Analysis 5–6* to reinforce or extend concepts and skills. "Recharge" skill review with the ready-to-go activities in this book, and give students the power to succeed!

Name ______________________________ Date ______________

Collecting Information

Match each term with its definition.

1. survey ________	**A.** group of people or items to be studied
2. population ________	**B.** part of the population selected to be surveyed
3. bias ________	**C.** collection and study of numbers of observations and the data drawn from these observations
4. frequency ________	**D.** number of times an event occurs
5. variable ________	**E.** information
6. statistics ________	**F.** asking people's opinion
7. inference ________	**G.** influence on a sample that keeps it from truly representing the population
8. sample ________	**H.** one of the choices or categories on a table or graph
9. data ________	**I.** conclusion formed after reviewing the data

A **biased** sample *does not* accurately represent the whole population.

A sample is **unbiased** if *every individual* in the population has an equal opportunity of being selected.

Identify each statement below as a **biased** or an **unbiased** sample.

10. ________ You survey 15 of your friends to see what activity they would like to do for your birthday party.

11. ________ A teacher sends out an Internet survey to find out how many students use the Internet for learning purposes.

12. ________ Viewers are asked to vote online for their favorite contestant.

13. ________ A computer randomly selects people from an extensive list to participate in a survey.

Name ______________________________ Date ______________

Ways to Collect Data

The four main methods of collecting data are the following:

A. in person　　**B.** by phone

C. by mail　　**D.** by e-mail or Internet

Read each statement. Write the letter of the method it describes. Some statements may have more than one answer.

1. ____________ A computer randomly selects people from an extensive list to participate in a survey.
2. ____________ This method requires many data collectors to conduct each survey.
3. ____________ This method allows the person responding to complete the survey at his or her convenience.
4. ____________ This method allows the person responding to ask questions about the survey as he or she is completing it.
5. ____________ This method allows the person responding to handwrite his or her responses.
6. ____________ The person responding may be more likely to lie or refuse to answer when this method is used.
7. ____________ This method allows a larger population to be interviewed in a shorter amount of time.
8. ____________ This method requires the person responding to own or use a computer.
9. ____________ There is a greater possibility that the survey will not be completed or returned with this method.
10. ____________ This method limits responses to the statements that are presented in the survey.

Name ______________________ Date ____________

Survey Says

The students in Mrs. Washington's fifth-grade class were asked to conduct a survey of the students at Fifth Street Elementary School to discover their preferences regarding the length of P.E. classes. 347 students attend the school.

The survey asked this question: *Do you think the number of minutes for each P.E. class should increase, decrease, or stay the same as they are now?*

Here are the results of Rhonda's survey:

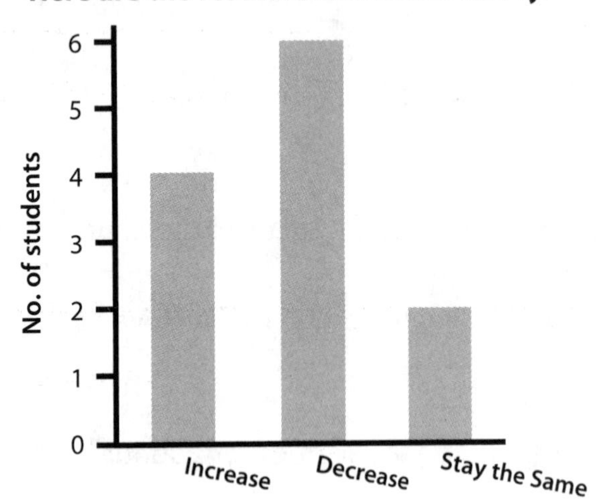

Here are the results of Mia's survey:

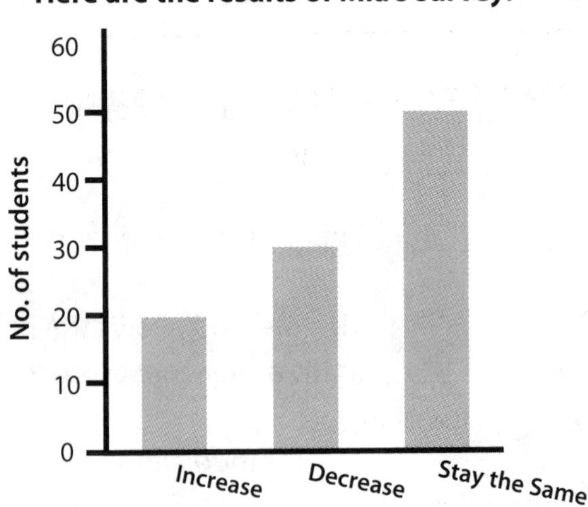

Answer the following questions.

1. What was the sample size of Rhonda's survey? ____________

2. What was the sample size of Mia's survey? ____________

3. How are the results of the two surveys different? Why do you think this occurred?

   ____

4. Which do you think more accurately reflects the entire population of students?

   Why? ____________

   ____

5. What inference can you make about the size of a sample surveyed? ____________

   ____

Name ______________________________ Date ______________

Watch Those Questions!

How a survey question is phrased is as important as the number of people you choose to survey. Questions need to include all possible responses, be unbiased, and be relevant to the topic surveyed in order to obtain the information you need.

Read the following survey questions. Tell why each would **not** make a good question. Then rewrite the questions and the answers so that they are unbiased, relevant, and include all possible responses.

1. How much TV do you watch in a week? **a)** 1–5 hours **b)** 6–10 hours **c)** 10–15 hours

____

____

2. Many unwanted pets end up in animal shelters. Do you think we should raise money for our local animal shelters?

____

____

3. How interested are you in science? **a)** extremely interested **b)** very interested **c)** interested

____

____

4. You root for the Tigers baseball team, don't you?

____

____

5. How old are you? **a)** under 10 **b)** under 20 **c)** under 30

____

____

Name ______________________________ Date ______________

Interpret a Tally Chart

A **tally chart** is a grid used to show information as it is collected. It uses tally marks to show numbers and a cross-through to show a set of five marks. The **frequency** is the total number of tally marks for a specific item.

Transportation to and from Georgetown Middle School	
walk	𝍸 𝍸 𝍸 𝍸 𝍸 𝍸 𝍸 𝍸 𝍸 𝍸 𝍸 𝍷𝍷𝍷
auto	𝍸 𝍸 𝍸 𝍸 𝍷𝍷𝍷𝍷
school bus	𝍸 𝍸 𝍸 𝍷𝍷𝍷𝍷
public bus	𝍷𝍷𝍷𝍷
bicycle	𝍸 𝍸 𝍸 𝍸 𝍸 𝍸 𝍷𝍷𝍷𝍷
other	𝍷𝍷

Solve.

1. Find the frequency for each choice:

   walk ________ auto ________ school bus ________

   public bus ________ bicycle ________ other ________

2. How do most students get to Georgetown Middle School? ____________________

3. What was the total number of students surveyed? ____________________

4. How many students rely on someone else to take them to and from school? ________
   Explain your answer.

   ____

5. Why does the survey include a category called "other"? ____________________

   ____

6. What inference can you make based on this tally chart? ____________________

   ____

Name ______________________________ Date ______________

Tally Ho!

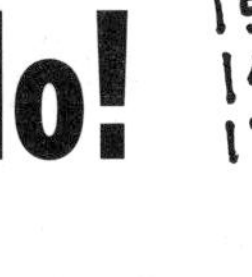

Record the data below using the tally chart.

Height of each student in the fifth grade (in centimeters):

132, 148, 141, 142, 141, 136, 133, 149, 138, 139, 142, 144, 145, 147, 148, 147, 152, 154, 137, 137, 150, 151, 146, 154, 147, 149, 152, 148, 149, 135, 151, 157, 156, 150, 139, 132, 147, 156, 146, 153, 144, 146, 141, 142, 135, 144, 145, 144, 149, 150, 136, 140, 157, 145

Height	Tally	Frequency
132 cm–134 cm		
135 cm–137 cm		
138 cm–140 cm		
141 cm–143 cm		
144 cm–146 cm		
147 cm–149 cm		
150 cm–152 cm		
153 cm–155 cm		
156 cm–158 cm		

Use the information in the chart to answer the following questions:

1. Which height range has the highest frequency? ______________________
2. Which height range has the lowest frequency? ______________________
3. What was the total population sampled? ______________________

   ____
4. Which height range has more kids: 138 cm–140 cm or 150 cm–152 cm? ______________
5. How many students were 147 cm or taller? ______________________
6. What inference can you make about the data on this chart? ______________________

   ____

Name ______________________________ Date ______________

Read a Pictograph

Pictographs are diagrams that organize and present data in a visual way. They use symbols that describe the topic of the data. Each symbol represents a fixed number. Partial symbols can be used to show smaller quantities.

Aluminum Cans Recycled

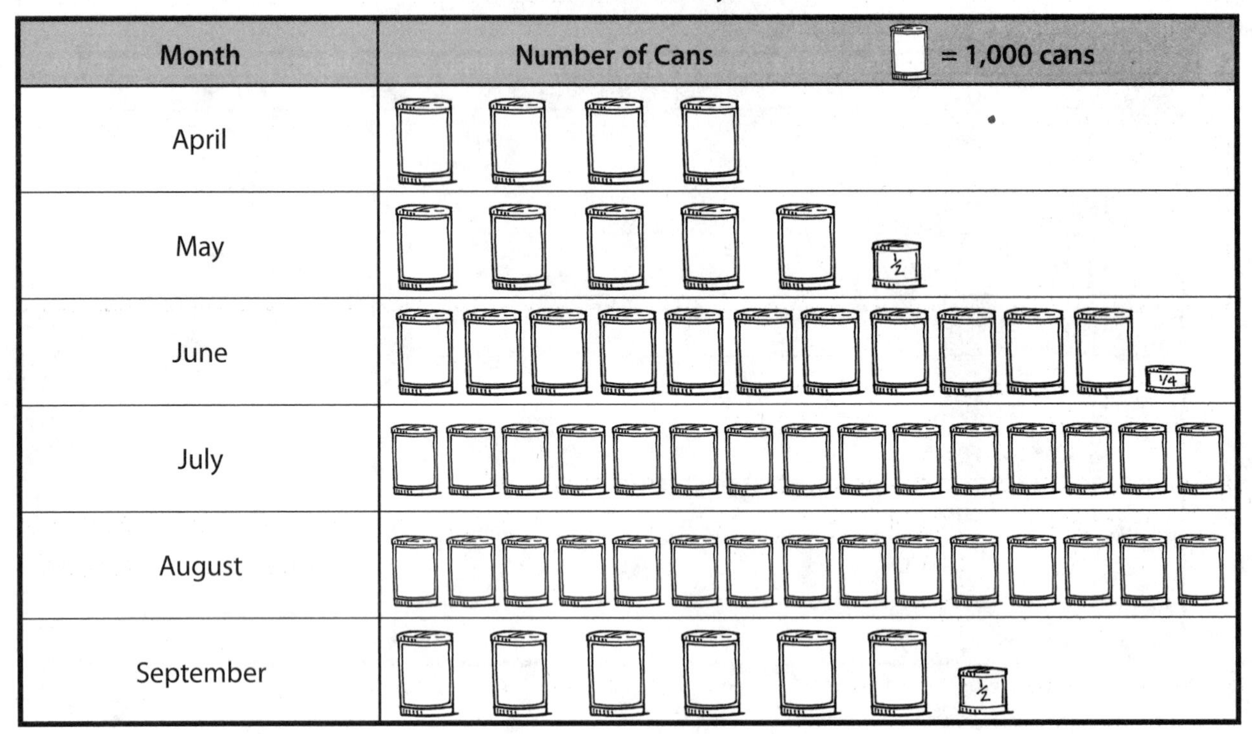

Solve.

1. How many cans were recycled in May? ______________________________
2. How many cans were recycled in June? ______________________________
3. What was the difference between the number of cans recycled in August and September?

   ____
4. What was the total number of cans recycled for these 6 months? ______________________________
5. Which months had the same totals? ______________________________
6. What inference can you make about the data on this chart? ______________________________

   ____

Name ______________________ Date ______________

Picture This

Annual Michigan Christmas Tree Harvest

Tree Species	Number of Trees (tree symbol) = 100,000 trees
Douglas fir	
Noble fir	
Scotch pine	
Fraser fir	
Blue spruce	
White spruce	
Other	

Use the data below to complete the pictograph.

1. Record on the graph the amount of each tree harvested.

Douglas fir	700,000	Noble fir	400,000	Scotch pine	2,000,000
Fraser fir	300,000	Blue spruce	600,000	White spruce	450,000
Other	550,000				

2. What is the total number of trees harvested annually in Michigan? ______________

3. Fraser firs are what percent of the total number of trees? ______________

4. How many more Scotch pines are harvested than the next largest amount? ______________

5. The category "Other" includes red pines, which are 3% of the total number of trees. If you were to add this to the graph, how many symbols would you add? ______________

6. What inference can you make from this graph? ______________

____

____

____

Name ______________________________ Date ______________

Read a Table

Use the information provided in the table to answer the questions.

Christmas Tree Light Sets Sold

Pattern	Multicolored	Clear
Blinking	8	6
Solid	15	22
Fade in-out	14	10

1. What are the categories listed in the table graph? ______________________________

____

2. List the variables in the pattern category. ______________________________

____

3. How many sets were sold that have a fade in-out pattern and are multicolored?

____

4. Which sets are more popular, multicolored or clear? ______________________

5. If all the light sets cost the same amount to manufacture and were sold at the same price, which set was the most profitable?

____

Name ______________________________ Date ______________

Temperature Table

Use the information provided in the table to answer the questions.

First 6-month Average Temperature and Rainfall for Chicago, Illinois
(Temperatures stated in degrees °F and rainfall in inches)

Month	Average High	Average Low	Avg. Rainfall	Record High	Record Low
January	32	18	2.17	67 (1950)	–24 (1985)
February	38	24	1.77	71 (1976)	–12 (1951)
March	47	32	3.01	84 (1986)	0 (1962)
April	59	42	3.65	91 (1986)	13 (1982)
May	70	51	3.70	94 (1991)	32 (1954)
June	80	61	4.30	104 (1988)	41 (1972)

Solve.

1. What is the average rainfall for the first six months of the year in Chicago?

   ____

2. The record low temperature in Chicago during the first six months of the year was in January 1985. When was the record high temperature? ______________________________

3. Find the average high and low temperatures for the spring months of March, April, and May. Round to the nearest tenth. ______________________________

4. What could you conclude about the temperatures between 1985 and 1988? ______________

   ____

Name ______________________ Date ____________

Raising the Table

Based on the information provided, complete the table.

Class Fund-raiser Results

Items	Price	Start Item Count	End Item Count	Items Sold	Total Amount
Cookies	$.10	24	2	22	
Brownies	$.20		0		$4.80
Lemonade	$.25	50 cups	22 cups		
Water Bottles	$.75	48	28		
Pencils	$.15	50		45	$6.75
Artwork	$2.00	15	10		
				Grand Total:	

Solve.

1. What was the total amount earned by selling 22 cookies? Fill in your answer on the table.

2. If 45 pencils were sold, what is the end item count? Fill in your answer on the table.

3. Fill in the remainder of the table by calculating the missing numbers using the information provided.

4. Since all the items were donated to the class, how much did the class earn in their fund-raiser? Fill in your answer in the Grand Total.

Name ______________________________ Date ______________

Election Results

From the information provided, complete the table.

____

1. An election for class president was held in your school. Grades 1 through 6 voted. The header line, the top row of the table, should include candidate name, each grade, and total votes. Be sure to put a title above your table.

2. There were five candidates for class president: John, Chuck, Aleesha, Helen, and Jose. Fill in their names in the first column of the table.

3. The results for each candidate are listed here in order for grades 1 through 6. Add the information to the table.

   John: 14; 21; 7; 5; 2; 0
   Chuck: 20; 10; 15; 8; 5; 3
   Aleesha: 3; 12; 23; 18; 25; 21
   Helen: 17; 2; 2; 1; 1; 0
   Jose: 5; 6; 9; 17; 18; 28

4. Add the results to get the total for each candidate, and enter it in the table.

5. What can you conclude based on the information in the table? ______________________________

____

Name ______________________________ Date ______________

Read a Bar Graph

Based on the information, answer the questions.

Lost and Found
Total Items Lost (School Year 2007)

50				
40				
30				
20				
10				
	Gloves	Hats	Sweaters	Backpacks

Solve.

1. How many gloves were turned in during the school year of 2007? ______________
2. How many backpacks were turned in that year? ______________
3. What is the ratio of hats to backpacks? ______________
4. How do you know which item was turned in most often? ______________

   ____
5. What item did students seem to lose the most? ______________
6. Not all items found would be placed on the list. How many of an item needs to be turned in before it is recorded on the list? ______________

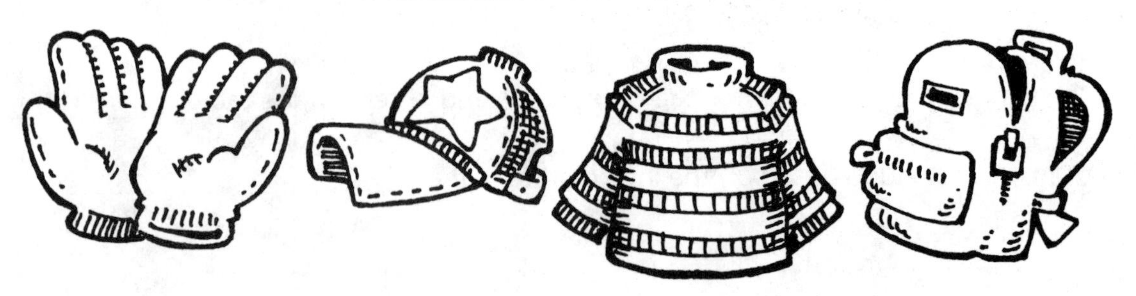

Name ________________________________ Date ______________

Fill It In

Based on the information given, complete the bar graph.

Class Birthdays

Number of Birthdays

15												
14												
13												
12												
11												
10												
9												
8												
7												
6												
5												
4												
3												
2												
1												
	Jan.	Feb.	Mar.	Apr.	May	June	July	Aug.	Sept.	Oct.	Nov.	Dec.

Months

Solve.

1. Why do the numbers in the first column increase from the bottom to the top? ______________

   ____

2. How many students have their birthday in April? __________ How many in May? __________

3. There are 30 students in the class. If 10% of the class has their birthday in June, how many would you enter on the graph? Enter the amount by coloring the month column. __________

4. October and December have 6.67% each. With 30 students in the class, how many birthdays would you put for each month? Enter it on the graph. __________

5. In what months are there no birthdays? ______________________________

Name ______________________________ Date ______________

Vertical or Horizontal?

Look at the two different bar graphs. Answer the questions based on the graphs.

Test Scores on Vertical Graph

Number of Students

50
40
30
20
10

A B C D F

Grade

Test Scores on Horizontal Graph

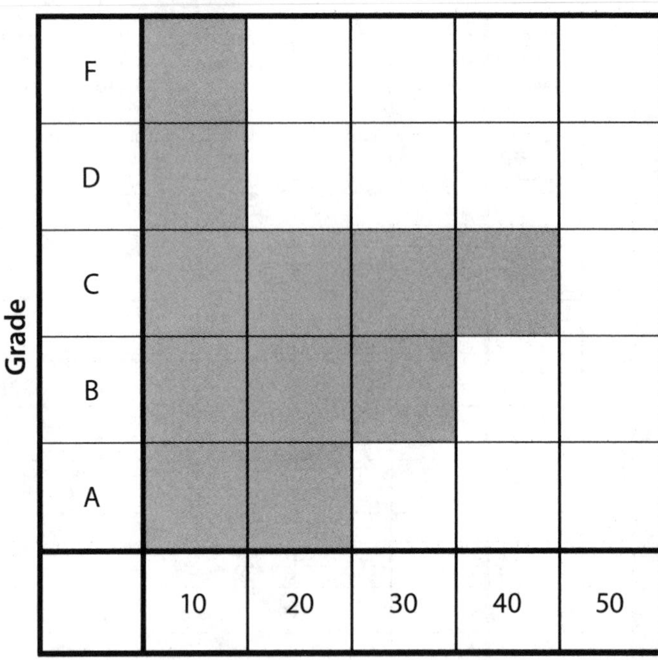

Number of Students

Solve.

1. On the Vertical Graph, what are the variables on the y-axis? ______________________

2. On the Horizontal Graph, what are the variables on the x-axis? ______________________

3. Look at both graphs. What is the difference between the two? What are the similarities?

____

____

4. How many students received an A on their test, according to the vertical graph? ________

   According to the horizontal graph? ______________

5. What grade did most students receive? ______________

Name ______________________________ Date ____________

Make Your Own

Create a vertical graph based on the information given below.

____

Solve.

1. You conducted a survey and asked 15 of your friends which ice-cream flavor each one liked best: chocolate, vanilla, mint, strawberry, or cookies and cream. List the variables of your survey on the vertical and horizontal axis lines.

2. Title your graph.

3. Create the bars by coloring in the following amounts for the different flavors: 6 people picked chocolate, 3 picked cookies and cream, 4 picked vanilla, 1 picked strawberry, and 1 picked mint.

4. Write three questions that can be answered using the information from your graph.

____

____

____

Name ______________________________ Date ______________

Same Info Three Ways

Graphs 1, 2, and 3 show results from the same survey. Study the graphs and then answer the questions.

Grade 5 and 6 Field Trip

Graph 1

25					
20					
15					
10					
5					
	Zoo	Museum	Art Show	Water Park	Baseball Game

1 Name the three types of graphs.

____

____

____

2 Which graph shows the count variable by fives?

____

3 In the pictograph, there are 10 hands for the water park. How much is each hand worth?

____

4 Which graph shows that more of the 5th graders want to go to the zoo?

____

Graph 2

	Zoo	Museum	Art Show	Water Park	Baseball Game
grade 5	10	3	4	8	4
grade 6	5	2	1	12	6

Graph 3

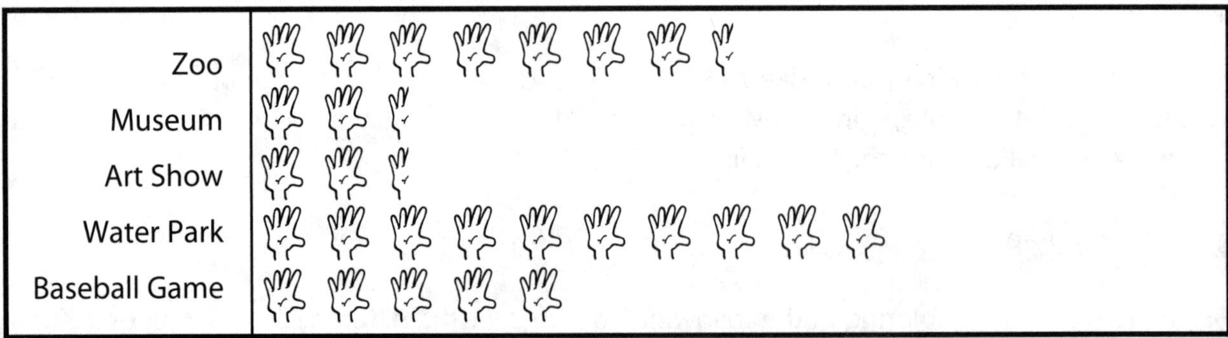

5 Does the table graph show that the same number of students want to go to the baseball game as is shown on the other graphs? Explain.

____

____

6 By analyzing all three graphs, which field trip do the students most want to take?

____

Name ______________________________ Date ______________

Read a Line Graph

The line graph shows your family's driving time on the freeway. You are traveling at an average speed of 60 miles per hour. Based on the line graph, answer the questions below.

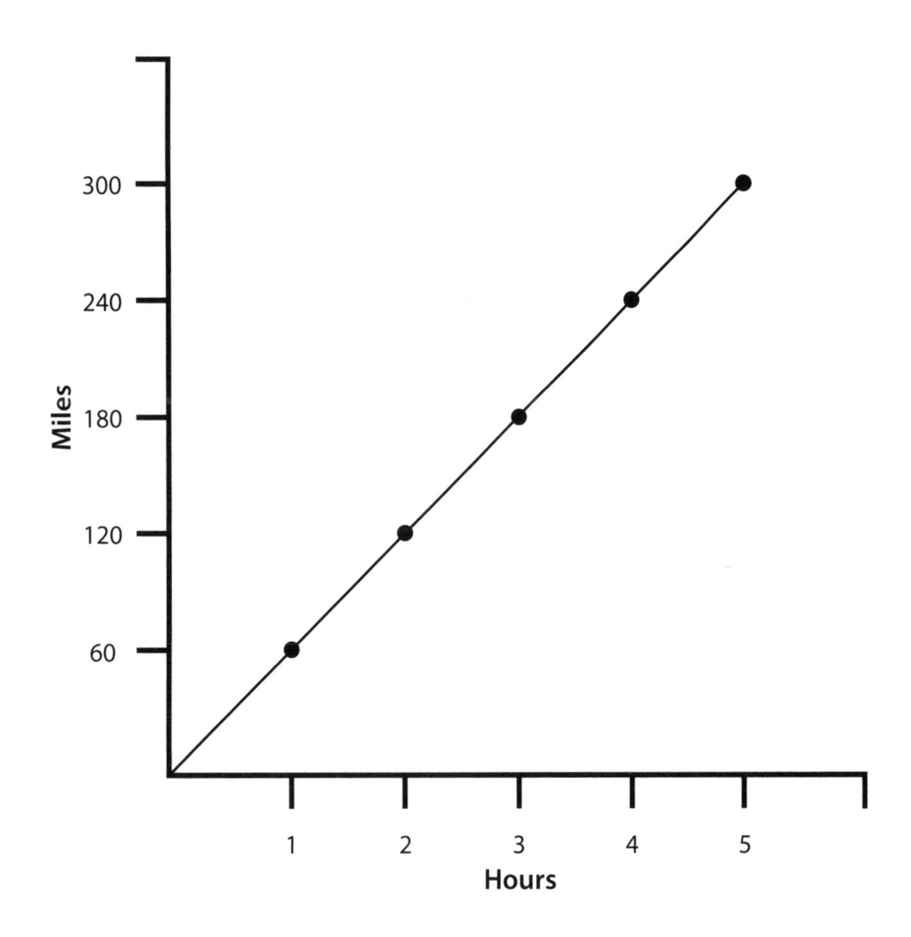

1. Where should zero be placed on the graph? ______________________________
2. How far did your family travel in one hour? ______________________________
3. How long will it take you to travel 300 miles? ______________________________
4. If your trip was only 210 miles, how long would it take to get there? ______________________________
5. If you stop for dinner after two hours and dinner takes an hour, how much longer will it take to complete a 240-mile trip?

____

Name ______________________________ Date ______________

Line It Up

Based on the information given, fill in the blank portions of the line graph by answering the questions below.

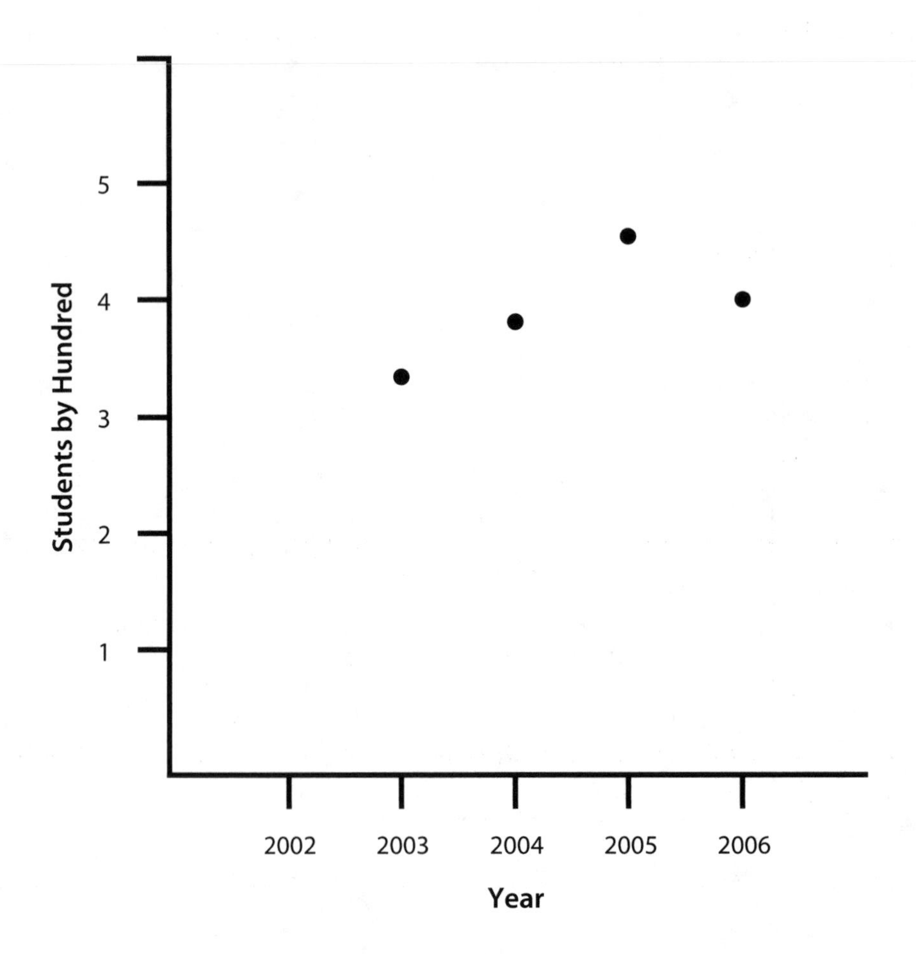

1. The variables on the y-axis state student enrollment. How many students would be represented by the number 2 on the y-axis? ______________________

2. In 2002, there were 300 students. Make a dot on the graph to mark that amount. Connect the enrollment marks on the graph to make a line graph.

3. The greatest enrollment was in 2005. How many students were there? ______________

4. What is the percentage of the increase of students from 2002 to 2005? ______________

5. What year was there a decline in enrollment? ______________

Name ______________________________ Date ______________

Bar Graph or Line?

Based on the information provided in the graphs, answer the questions below.

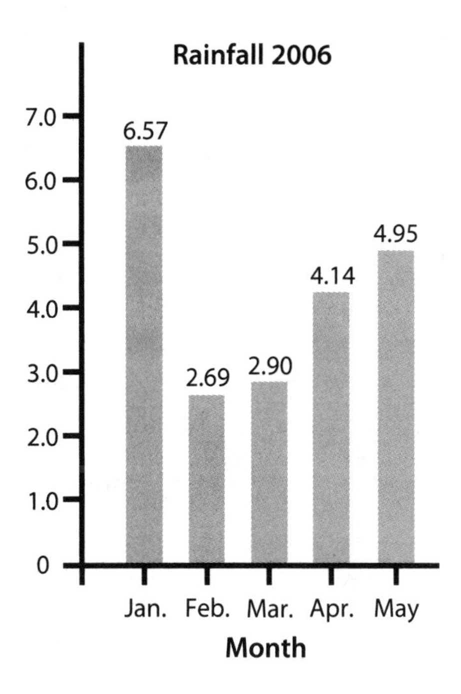

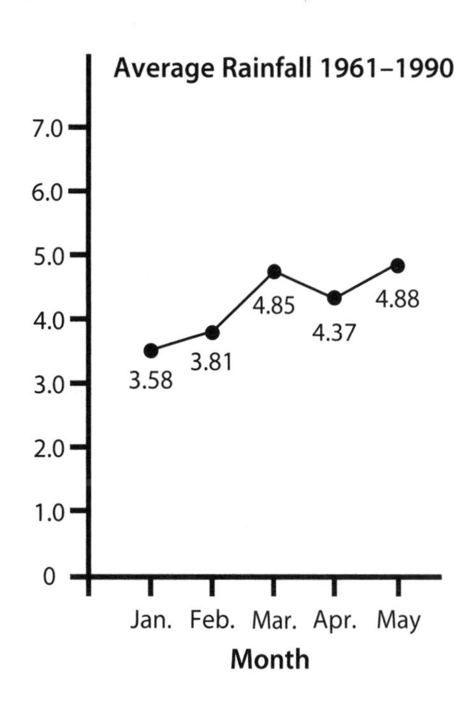

1. These two graphs show rainfall data for Nashville, Tennessee. What is the difference between the two graphs and the information?

   ____

2. What is the ratio of rainfall in January 2006 compared to the 30-year average? ______________

3. Which month has the most average rainfall? Which month had the most rainfall in 2006?

   ____

4. Which month in 2006 had the closest ratio of rainfall compared to its monthly average?

   ____

5. Which month in 2006 had the lowest amount of rainfall compared to its monthly average?

   ____

Name ______________________ Date ____________

Read a Pie Chart

Pie charts are also known as circle graphs. Based on the information provided in the pie charts, answer the questions below.

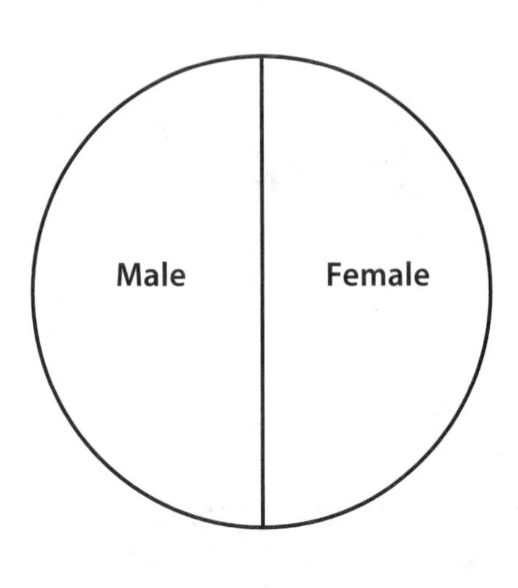

Graph 1

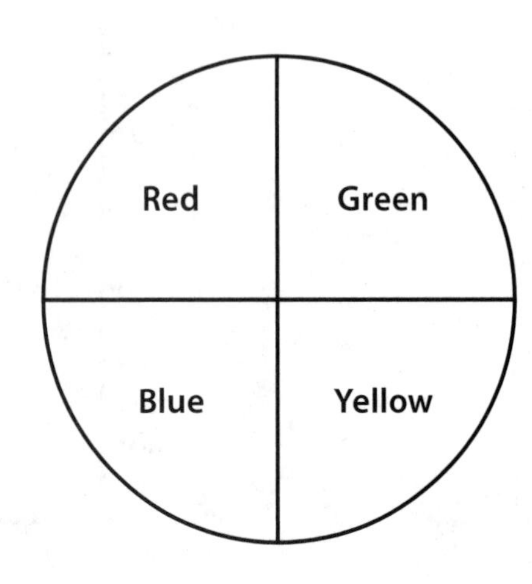

Graph 2

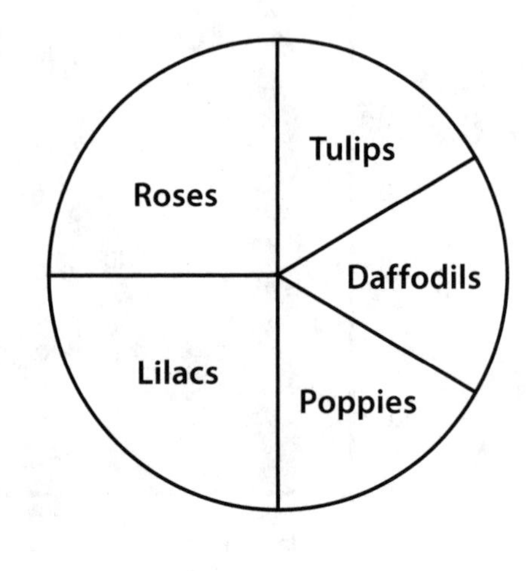

Graph 3

1. A circle graph represents 100% of the collected information. In Graph 1, what percent is male and what percent is female? ______________________

2. In Graph 2, what percent is the color yellow? Do the other colors have the same percentage?

   ____

3. How many types of flowers are recorded in Graph 3? ______________________

4. If the roses are 25% and the lilacs are 25%, what percent is the other three flowers combined in Graph 3? ______________________

5. In Graph 3, the flowers include equal amounts of tulips, daffodils, and poppies.

   What percent is each?______________________

6. Compare the three graphs. Which graph shows the largest percent for a single category?

   ____

Name ______________________________ Date ______________

A Circle Graph

Below are calculations that tell what is in a typical landfill in Iowa. Use this information along with the questions to complete the graph.

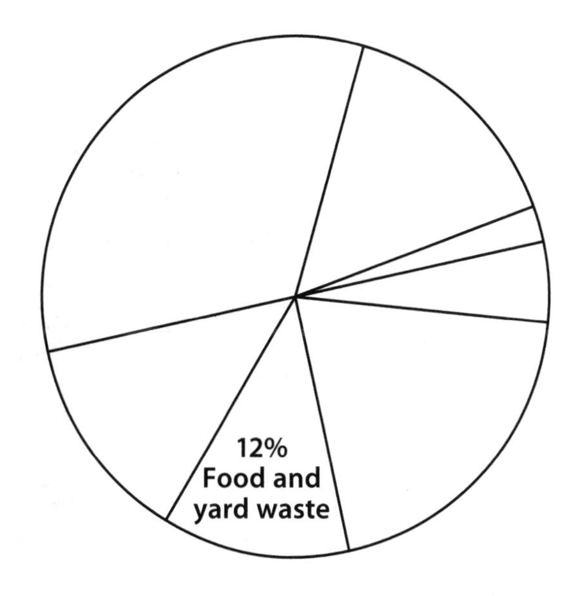

Paper	33%
Plastic	15%
Metals	5%
Glass	2%
Food and yard waste	12%
Wood and construction waste	13%
Other waste	20%

Note: *If there is not enough room to enter the name of the item along with the percent, write them outside the circle near the section and draw a line to where it belongs.*

1. Enter the three largest items of waste on the circle graph. In each portion, enter the percent.
2. What item has the next highest percentage? Enter it onto the graph.
3. Label remaining items with their names and percentages.
4. Which item creates the largest amount of waste? Which creates the smallest? ______________

   ____

5. Why is there a category called "Other waste"? What might be included in this category?

   ____

Name ______________________________ Date ______________

Recycle Circle Graph

A school poll was taken to determine the items students recycle. Based on the information provided, create a circle graph to show the results.

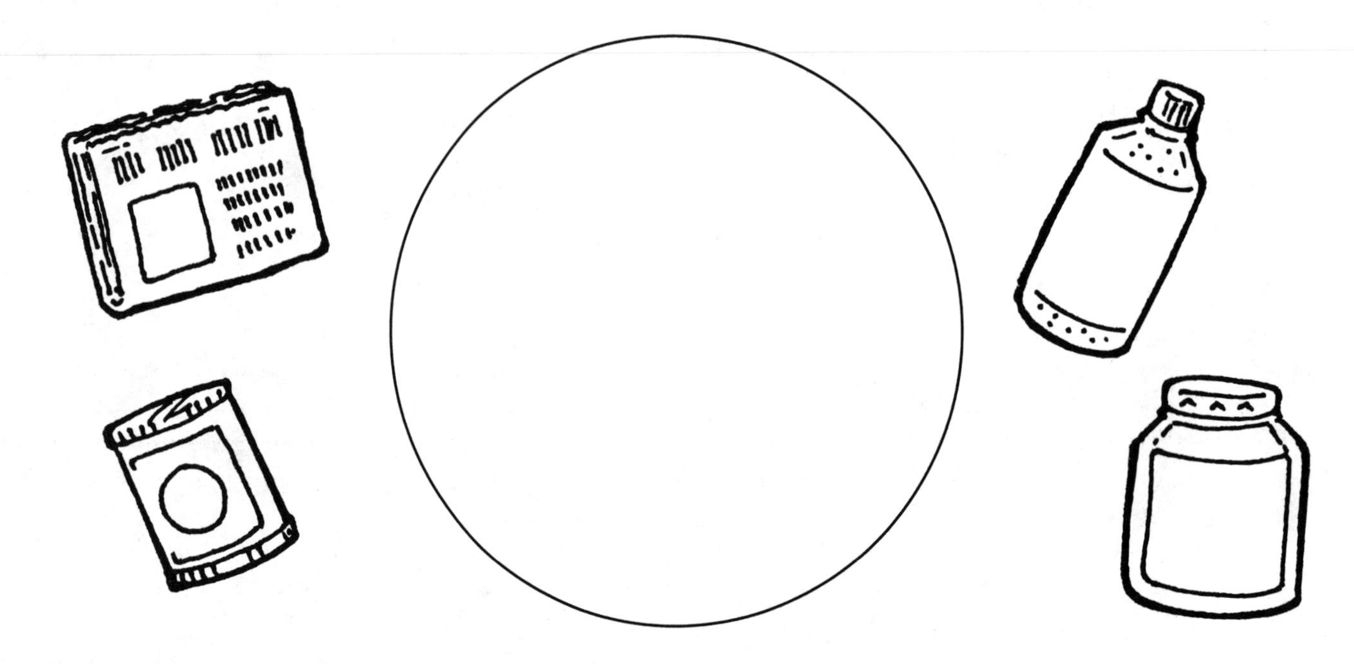

1. What would you title your circle graph? ______________________________

2. The results of the poll are as follows:

Cans	45 %
Glass Bottles	30 %
Paper	10 %
Cardboard	2 %
Plastic	13 %

What is the total? Why do they add up to this number? ______________________________

Note: *To help divide the circle graph into sections, draw a faint dotted line to divide the circle in half, both vertically and horizontally. Remember, one half of the circle is 50%. One quarter of a circle is 25%.*

3. Enter the results of the poll into the graph and label each part of the circle.

4. Cans are recycled more than glass bottles. What is the percent difference? ______________

5. By looking at the chart, what can you infer about the recycled items?

____

Name ______________________ Date ______________

Circle–Line–Bar Ranch

Based on the information provided in the graphs, answer the questions below.

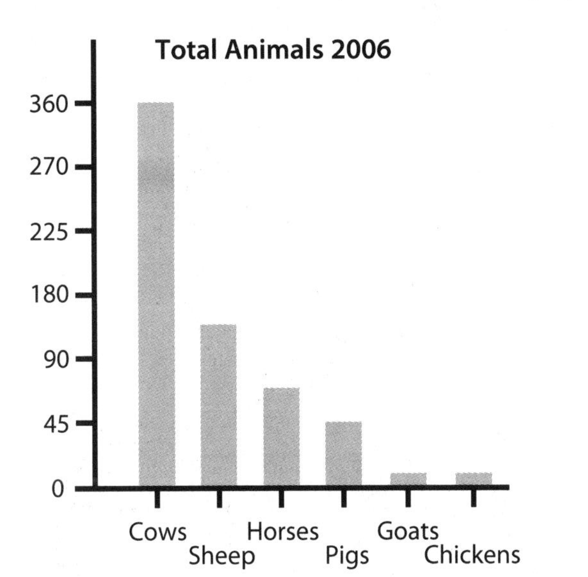

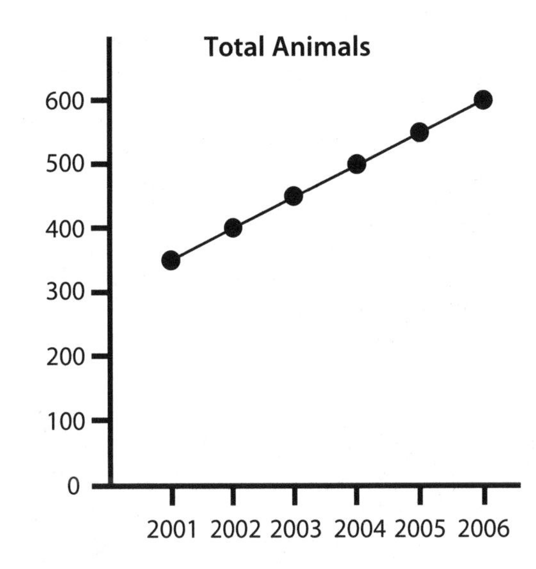

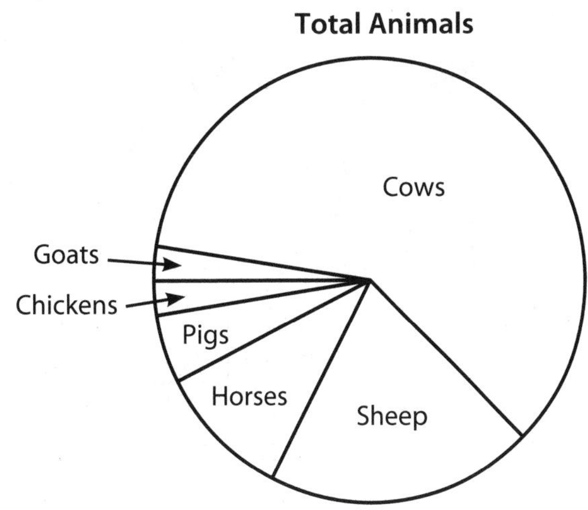

1. What animal would you most likely find on the ranch? ______________
2. In 2006, there were 600 animals. What percent were cows? ______________
3. In 2006, 10% of the animals were horses. How many horses were on the ranch? ______________
4. Which graph (or graphs) show the amounts in numbers? ______________
5. Which graph would you use to find the percent of each animal? ______________
6. Which graph shows the change in total number of animals per year? ______________

Name ______________________ Date ______________

Read a Strip Graph

A **strip graph** looks like a bar graph, but it shows information as a percentage. The data on the graph adds up to equal one whole, or 100%. The strips on the graph use shading to give different information.

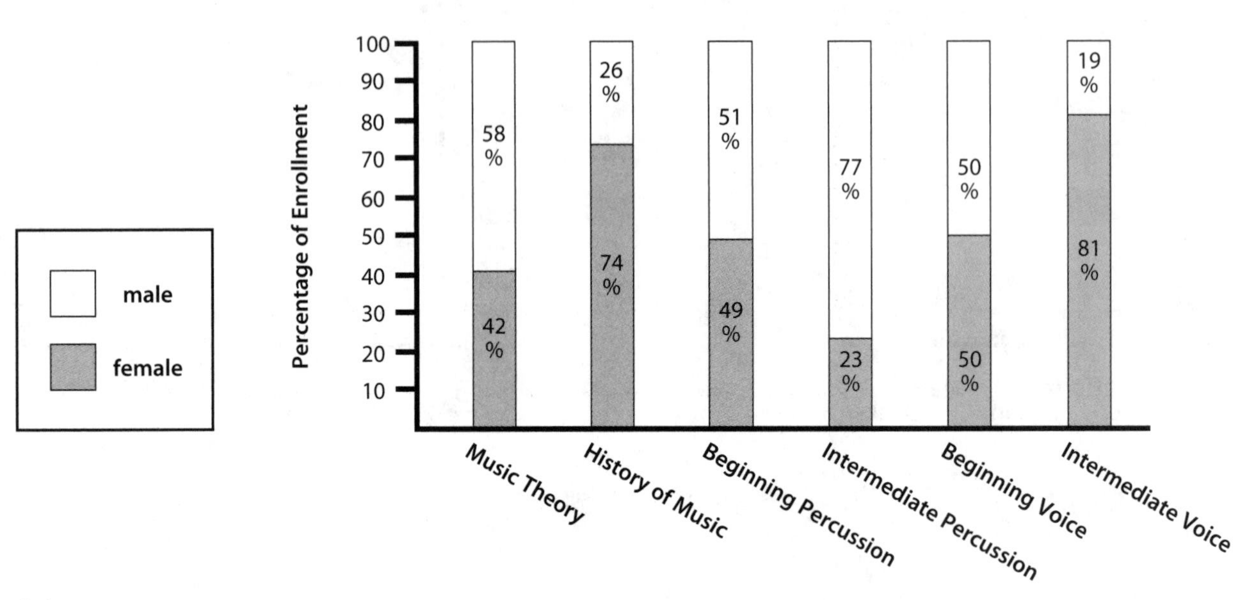

Solve.

1. Which class had a female enrollment of greater than 75%? ______________

2. How is the enrollment of the beginning percussion class different from that of the intermediate percussion class?

   ____

3. Which two classes were more popular with female students than with male students?

   ____

4. Which three classes were more popular with male students than with female students?

   ____

5. Which class had the same ratio of male students to female students? ______________

6. What inferences might you make from the results of this graph? ______________

   ____

Name ______________________________ Date ______________

A 100% Response

The sixth-grade classes must determine how they will spend the money budgeted for their grade. Each student was asked to vote yes for three things he or she wanted most on a list. Use the information below to complete the graph. Then answer the questions.

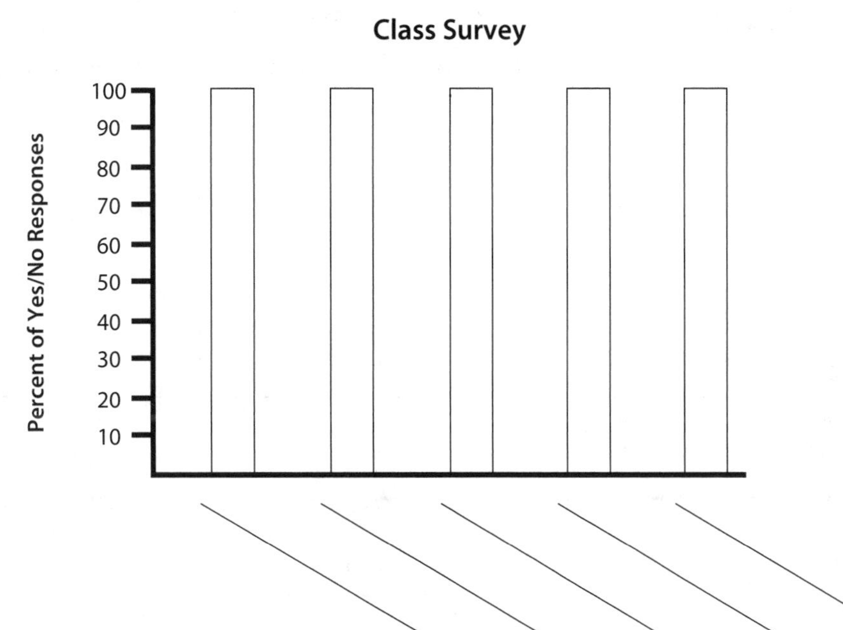

1. Record the following results on the chart:

Field Trip	56% no	Play Performance	28% no
Art Supplies	37% yes	Science Materials	92% yes
Graduation Party	76% no		

2. According to the results, on which three activities or things should the money be spent?

____

3. Compare the results for the field trip and the graduation party. Which did the students seem to feel more strongly about? Explain.

____

4. What was the difference between the percent of yes votes for the play performance and the yes votes for the art supplies?

____

5. Which choice seemed most popular among the students? ______________________________

6. What inferences might you make from the results of this graph? ______________________________

Name ______________________________ Date ______________

Conduct a Survey

Make a strip graph to display the responses to your own survey. Write four questions on a topic that can be answered yes or no, or ask for a choice between two items. Survey 20 people and record their responses. Show their responses on the strip graph.

Questions	Choice 1 / Yes	Choice 2 / No
1		
2		
3		
4		

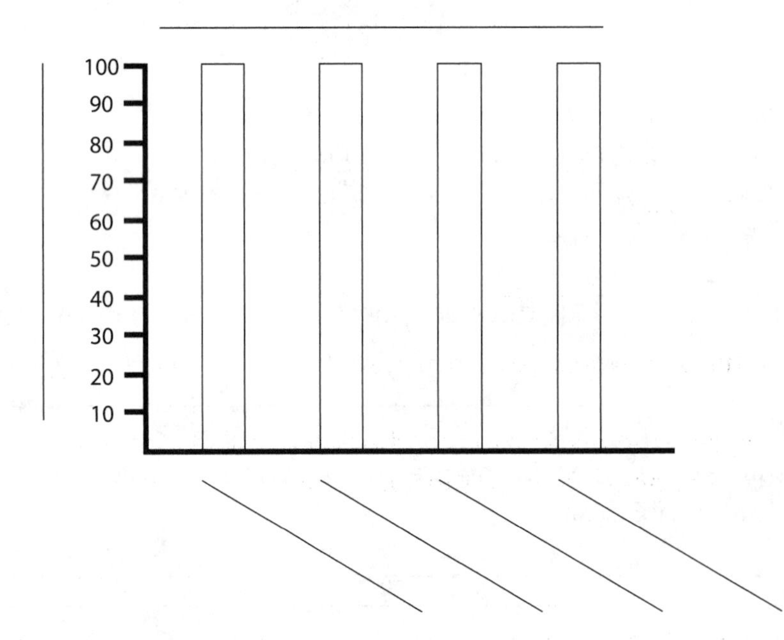

Write four statements that explain what someone can infer from your strip graph.

____

____

____

____

Name ______________________________ Date ______________

Choose the Best One

Answer the questions by choosing the graph that has the information you need.

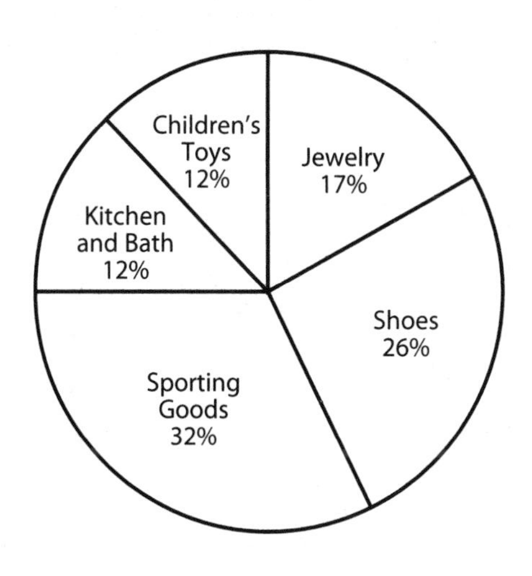

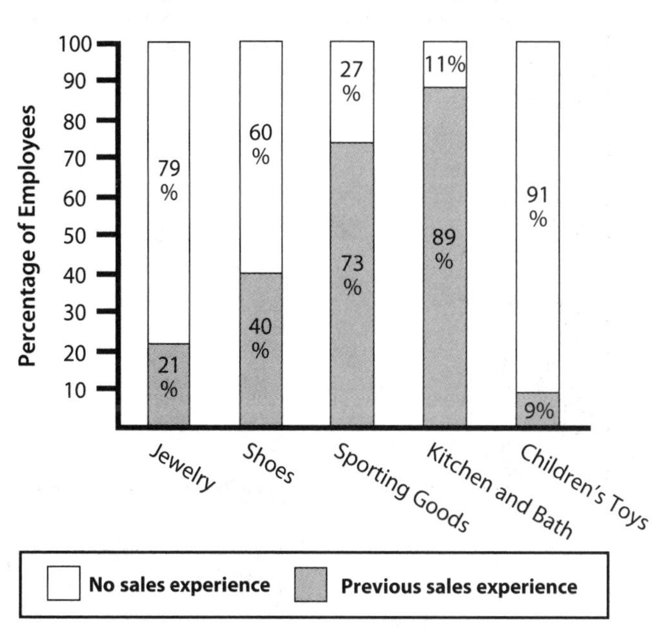

1. Which department's new employees have the most sales experience? What percent of that department lacks sales experience?

   ____

2. Which department hired the most new employees? ______________________________

3. Were more experienced employees hired for the Shoe Department or the Jewelry Department? What is the percent difference between the two departments?

   ____

4. What was the difference between the percent of new employees for Children's Toys and new employees for Sporting Goods? ______________________________

5. If you knew that 50 people had been hired overall, how many employees were hired for the Shoe Department? For the Sporting Goods Department? ______________________________

6. What inferences can you make using the information from these two graphs?

   ____

Name ______________________________ Date ______________

Read a Line Plot

A **line plot** is a graph that shows frequency of data along a number line. An **outlier** is a number or numbers that occur the least on a line plot.

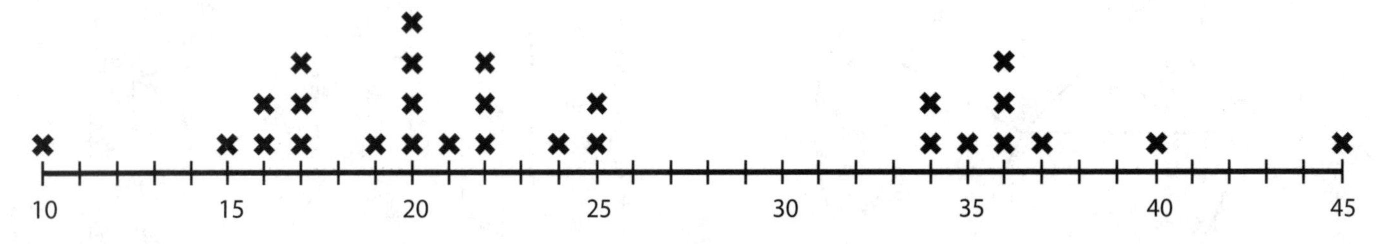

Ages of Chess Tournament Players

1. What is the scale of this graph? ______________________________
2. Which ages occur most frequently? ______________________________
3. What are the outliers on this graph? Why might these outliers occur? ______________________________

   ____
4. What clusters do you see? What would be the reason for this? ______________________________

   ____
5. What gaps occur on this line plot? ______________________________
6. What is the average age of the players? ______________________________
7. What were the ages of the oldest and youngest players at the tournament? ______________________________

   ____

Name ______________________________ Date ______________

Plot a Spot

Record the data on the line plot. Then use the line plot to answer the questions.

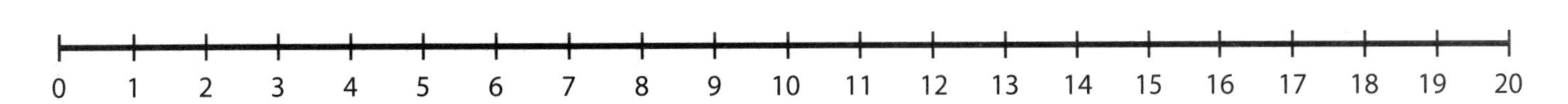

Number of Pets Owned by Mrs. Wilkes's Students

1. In Mrs. Wilkes's class, students were asked to give the number of pets owned by their family. Place their responses on the number line.

   0, 3, 13, 2, 2, 0, 4, 5, 2, 2, 1, 2, 1, 1, 3, 7, 1, 6, 4, 3, 2, 2, 2, 1, 4, 2, 3, 3, 1

2. What are the outliers, if any, on this line plot? Explain why these outliers may have occurred.

   ____

3. Are there any gaps on this line plot? Where do they occur? ______________

4. Are there any clusters that appear on this line plot? Where do they occur? ______________

5. What is the average number of pets owned by the students? ______________

6. Toss out the outlier. How does that change your average? ______________

   ____

Name ______________________________ Date ______________

Choose the Right One

The graphs give information about Crest City in 2004. Use the graph that gives you the correct information to answer each question.

Population

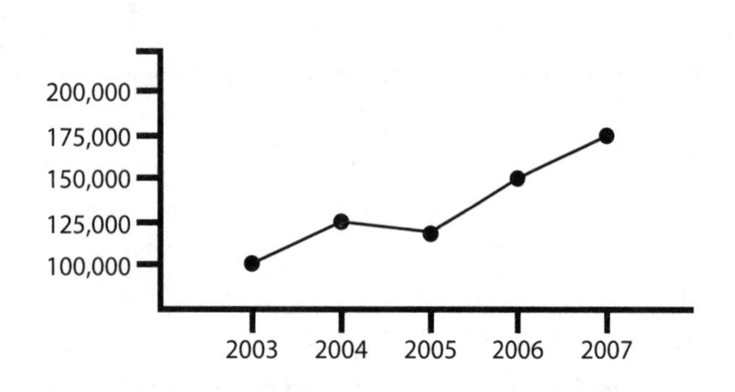

Age of Population

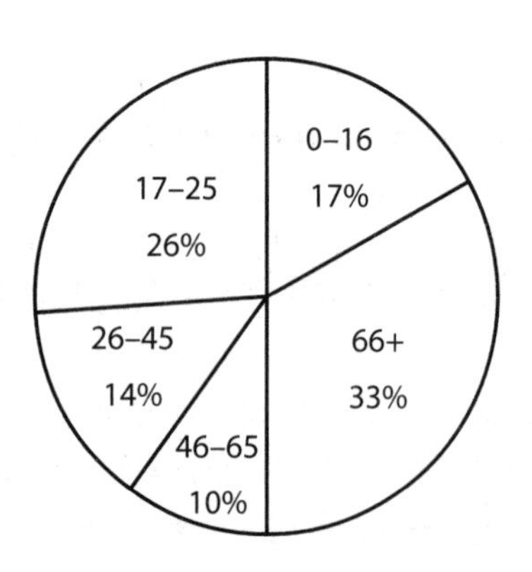

1. In what year did the population drop? ______________________________
2. Would you expect the population to increase or decrease in coming years? Explain.

   ____

3. How much larger is the 66-and-over group than the 16-and-under group? ______________
4. Approximately how many people lived in Crest City in 2004? ______________________
5. If there were an increase in births in 2008, which graph(s) would be affected by this new information? Why?

   ____

Name ______________________ Date ____________

Find an Average

To find an **average,** add the numbers together.

1 + 2 + 3 + 4 + 5 = 15

Then divide by how many numbers you added.

15/5 = 3

3 is the **average** of the five numbers added together.

Averages are used in many applications. Grades, temperatures, and rainfall are often given as averages. Find the averages in the following problems. Show your work.

1. There are 10 cows in one field, 5 in another, and 15 in the field by the barn. Each field is one acre. How many cows are there? What is the average number of cows per acre?

   ____

2. The low temperatures for the first week in January were 18, 20, 26, 22, 20, 23, and 21 degrees. What was the average low temperature for that week? Round to the nearest tenth.

   ____

3. The perfect score on the math test is 20. Of the 6 students that took the test, there were two 14s, a 5, two 17s and a 20. What was the average test score?

   ____

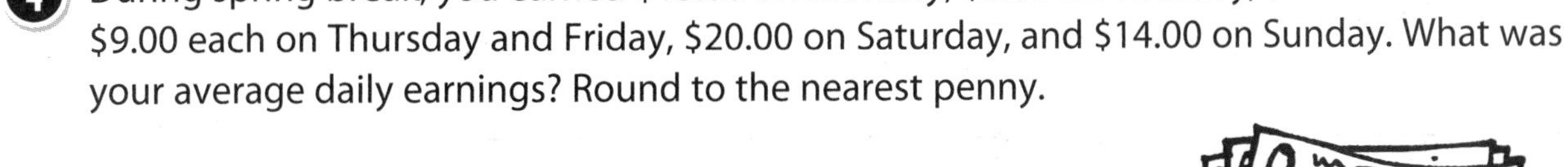

4. During spring break, you earned $13.00 on Monday, $5.00 on Tuesday, $4.00 on Wednesday, $9.00 each on Thursday and Friday, $20.00 on Saturday, and $14.00 on Sunday. What was your average daily earnings? Round to the nearest penny.

   ____

Name ______________________________ Date ______________

An Average Trip

You are preparing for a trip. You want to know what the temperatures are like so you know how to pack. By looking up the average temperature for when you are likely to visit a town, you can predict how the weather will be.

Reno, Nevada—Average Daytime Temperatures
1999 through 2003

Year	Jan.	Feb.	Mar.	Apr.	May	June	July	Aug.	Sep.	Oct.	Nov.	Dec.
1999	49.1	50.7	57.6	58.6	73.4	83.0	91.4	86.3	83.5	74.9	62.7	49.4
2000	48.7	51.4	59.0	69.0	74.9	88.3	91.0	90.9	80.9	66.8	50.1	49.9
2001	44.3	47.4	62.5	61.5	83.0	86.0	90.6	94.9	85.5	74.9	57.4	44.7
2002	45.5	54.4	56.3	65.7	73.9	86.9	95.7	89.9	83.2	68.6	56.6	48.1
2003	55.4	49.7	59.9	56.9	74.8	88.1	96.7	90.0	85.5	76.2	51.6	46.7

Solve.

1. Find the lowest average temperature for June. What is it and in what year did it happen?

   ____

2. The hottest monthly average temperature occured in which month and year? ______________

   In which month and year did the coldest average temperature occur? ______________

3. Find the average temperature for July over all five years. ______________

4. For all five years, what is the average temperature for December? January? February? Which month was the coldest?

   ____

5. Using the data on the chart, when would you want to visit Reno, Nevada? Explain.

   ____

   ____

Name ______________________ Date ____________

Mean, Median, and Average

The **mean** of a set of numbers is also called an average.
The **median** of a set of numbers is the number in the middle when the numbers are placed in order from smallest to largest. If you have an **even set** of numbers, then the median is the average of the two middle numbers in the order.

Solve.

1. There are twenty students. Ten are 11 years old, seven are 10 years old, one is 9 years old, and two are 12 years old. What is the mean age of these students?

____

2. What is the median age of the students listed in Problem 1? ______________________

3. You walk into class, and these numbers are written on the board:

If your teacher asked you what the median number is, what would be your answer?

____

4. The boys' basketball team played six games last season. The team's point totals in the games were as follows:

Game 1: 54 points
Game 2: 44 points
Game 3: 58 points
Game 4: 46 points
Game 5: 61 points
Game 6: 53 points

What was the team's mean score for the season? ______________________

Name ______________________ Date ____________

Mean, Median, Mode, and Range

The **mode** of a set of numbers is the number that is repeated the most.

The **range** is the highest number minus the lowest number.

Solve.

1. There are twenty students. Ten are 11 years old, seven are 10 years old, one is 9 years old, and two are 12 years old. What age would represent the mode?

____

2. When at the park, you notice all the different types of shoes the children wear. You decide to count the different types and came up with these numbers:

Tennis shoes	20	Dress shoes	5
Sandals	10	Hi-tops	8
Boots	7	Slip-ons	10

Which shoes would be the mode? ______________________

3. Here are the point totals for the girls' volleyball games this season:

15, 21, 18, 12, 11, 14, 21, 16, 21, 18, 9, 11, 21, 11, 19

What is the mean? What is the median? What is the mode? What is the range?

____

4. You surveyed many students in your school by asking: *Do you like to go to the movies?* Here were the counts of those students who said yes:

Grade 1: 15	Grade 2: 10	Grade 3: 12
Grade 4: 18	Grade 5: 19	Grade 6: 21

What would the range be for those that answered yes? ______________________

Name ____________________ Date ____________

Read a Stem-and-Leaf Plot

A **stem-and-leaf plot** graph shows numerical data arranged by place value. Using a stem-and-leaf plot makes finding the range, mode, and median easier.

Highest Point Totals by Basketball Players

Tens	Ones
6	0
5	0 1 2
4	0 1 3
3	0 0 2 5 8
2	0 4 4 4 4 5 7 8 9
1	0 2 2 5 5 6 8
0	8 9

Solve. Round answers to the nearest whole number.

1. The stem-and-leaf plot shows the points scored by the leading scorers in various games during the 2007 season. How many players' scores are recorded on the plot?

 ____

2. The largest number of players scored within what point range? ____________

3. What are the extreme values on this plot? ____________

4. What is the range for this data? ____________

5. What is the mean, median, and mode of the data? ____________

6. What inferences can you make about the scores of basketball players based on this plot?

 ____

 ____

Name ______________________________ Date ______________

Put Leaves on the Stem

Record the data on the stem-and-leaf plot. Then answer the questions.

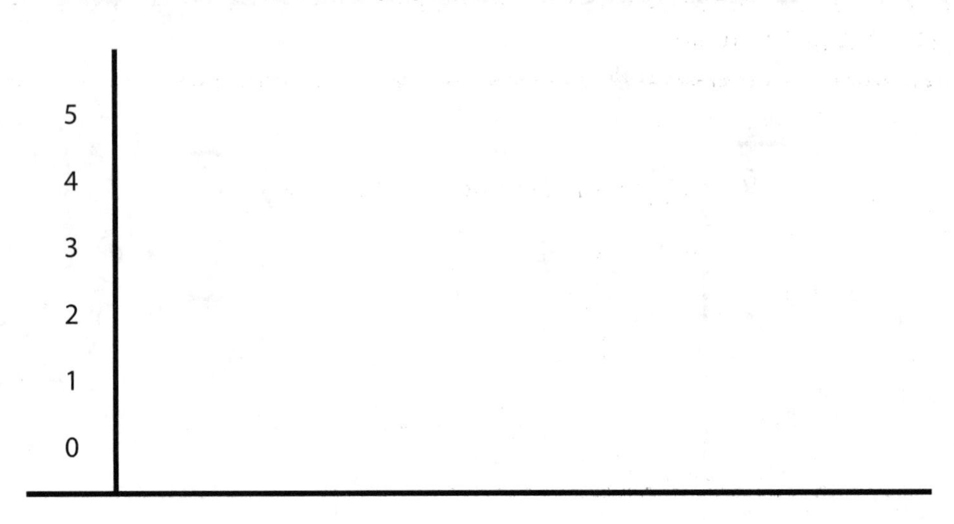

Solve.

1. The data shows the number of laps run by two classes. Place this data on the stem-and-leaf plot. Place the numbers in order from least to greatest.

   32, 4, 30, 22, 40, 50, 34, 15, 18, 26, 31, 40, 49, 54, 10, 11, 13, 31, 35, 34, 26, 51, 45, 23, 46, 51, 13, 13, 28, 32, 47, 48, 37, 36, 37, 33

2. How many student scores are recorded on the graph? ______________________

3. What are the extremes on this plot? Which one would you consider an outlier? Explain.

   ____

4. What is the range for this data? ______________________

5. What is the mean, median, and mode of the data? ______________________

6. What inferences can you make about the number of laps students ran based on this plot?

   ____

Name ______________________________ Date ______________

Read a Box Plot

A **box plot** is a way to visually show the median, extremes, greatest concentration, and range of a set of numbers. The **median** is found by listing the data values in increasing order, and finding the center value. This number forms the interior line of the box. The **lower quartile** forms the bottom line of the box. The **upper quartile** forms the top line of the box. These three lines are connected horizontally to form the sides of the box. The lowest value in the data set is called the **lower extreme.** The highest value is called the **upper extreme.**

Number of Books Read by 15 Students

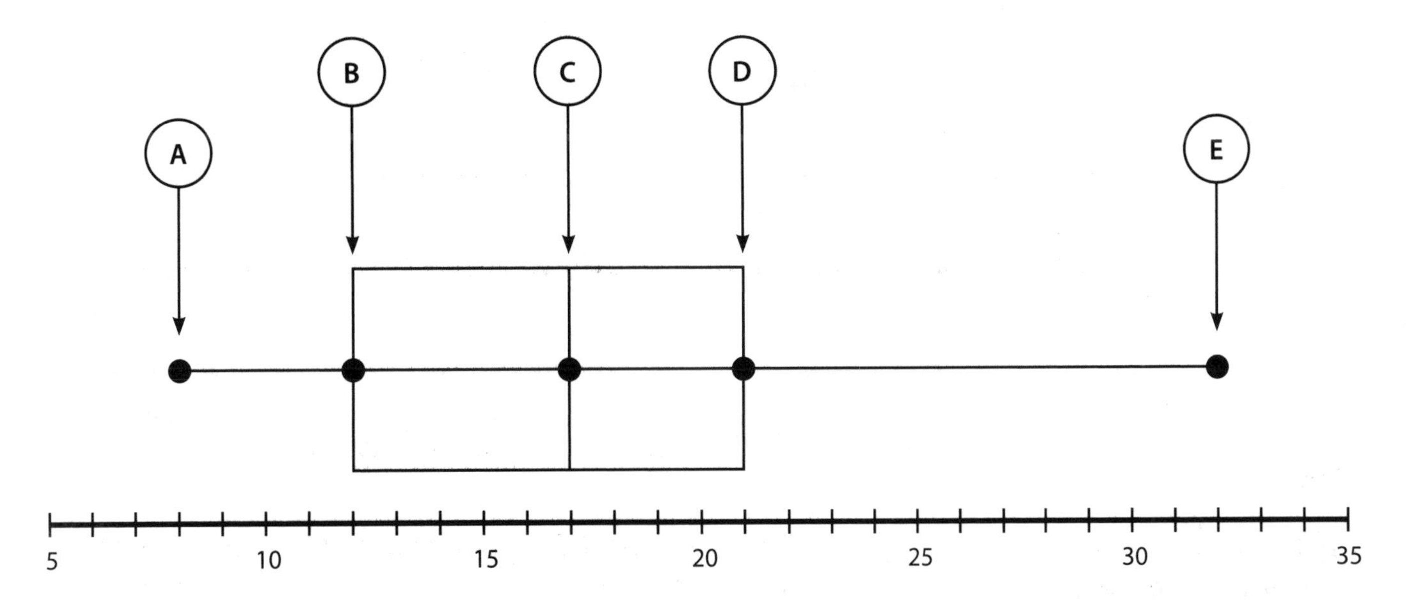

1 Match the box plot terms with the letters on the diagram.

_____ median _____ lower quartile _____ upper quartile

_____ upper extreme _____ lower extreme

2 What number is the median? ______________________

3 What number is the lower extreme of the range? ______________________

4 What number is the upper extreme of the range? ______________________

5 What numbers represent the lower and upper quartile of the box plot? ______________

Name ______________________ Date ____________

Make a Box Plot

This is a list of the temperatures recorded periodically in April.

37, 44, 44, 45, 52, 54, 60, 56, 52, 53, 48, 46, 45, 46, 43

Temperatures in April

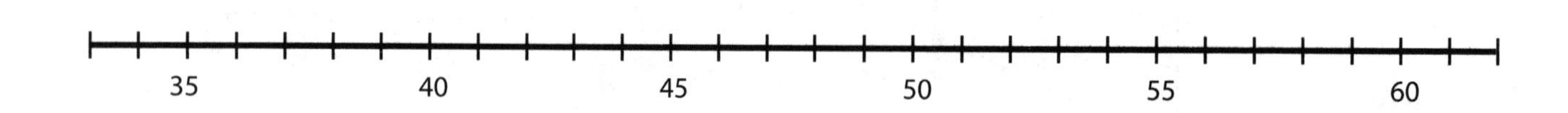

1. Rewrite the numbers in order. What is the median? ______________________
2. What are the high extreme and the low extreme? What is the range?

   ____
3. What is the lower quartile? What is the upper quartile? ______________________
4. What is the interquartile range? ______________________
5. Use the data above to make a box plot on the number line above. Is the data skewed?

   ____
6. What can you infer from this data? ______________________

   ____

Name ______________________________ Date ______________

Read a Histogram

A **histogram** looks similar to a vertical bar graph. A histogram has one variable, and data is sorted into categories of this one variable. The range of your variable is important. If the range is too wide or too narrow, it may be difficult to interpret the data.

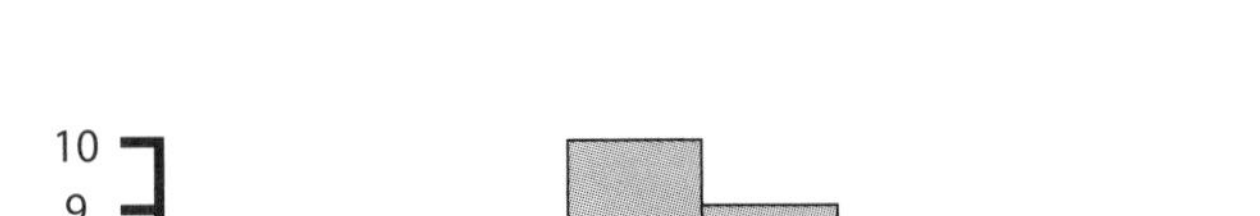

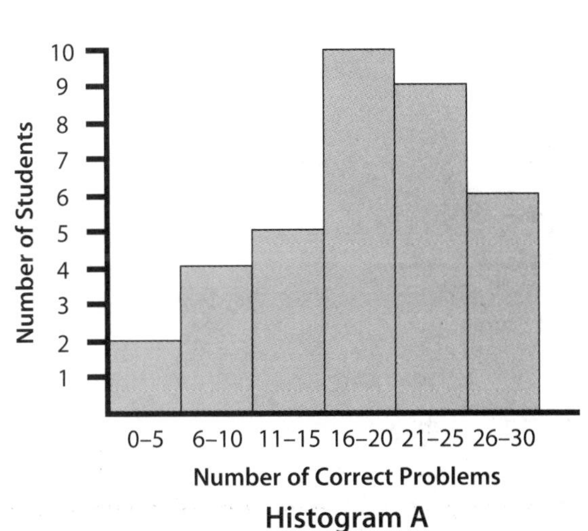

Histogram A

Histogram B

Solve.

1. How many students got between 16 and 20 problems correct?
   Which histogram(s) gives you this answer? ______________________________

2. How many students got between 21 and 30 problems correct?
   Which histogram(s) gives you this answer?

   ____

3. Both histograms show the results of the same math test. How are the two histograms different? How are they the same?

   ____

4. Which histogram gives more useful data? Explain.

   ____

5. How could you change the histogram to better show those students who received a passing score?

   ____

Name ______________________________ Date ______________

Same Story, Different Plots

This **histogram** and **box plot** both show student scores for a recent spelling test. An **outlier** is any value that lies more than one and a half times the length of the box from either end of the box. Outliers are usually marked with an asterisk.

Student Spelling Scores

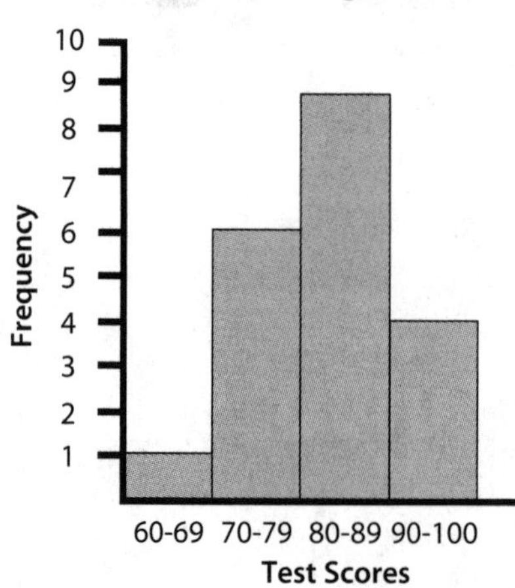

Student Spelling Scores

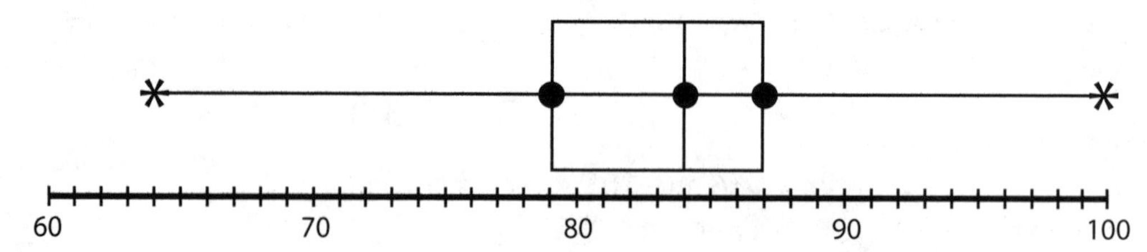

Solve.

1. What was the median test score? ______________
2. Most students scored within what scale? ______________
3. What is the range of the test scores? ______________
4. Are there any outliers? What are they? ______________
5. Which plot gives you a better idea of the number of students that received a passing score of 70 or above? ______________
6. What inferences can you make from these plots? ______________

____

Name ______________________________ Date ______________

The Best Choice

Identify the graph that would be best for each application.

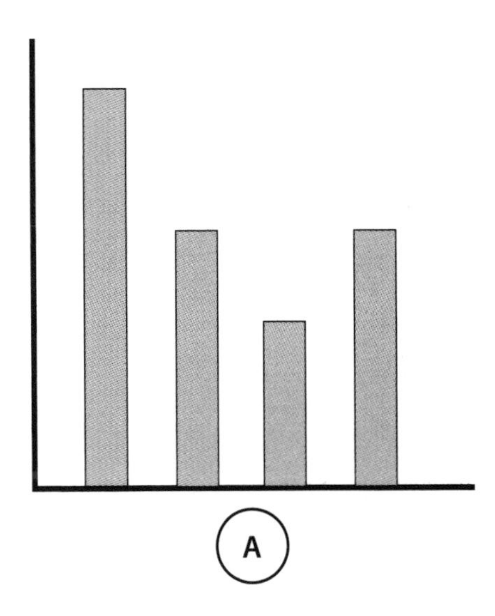

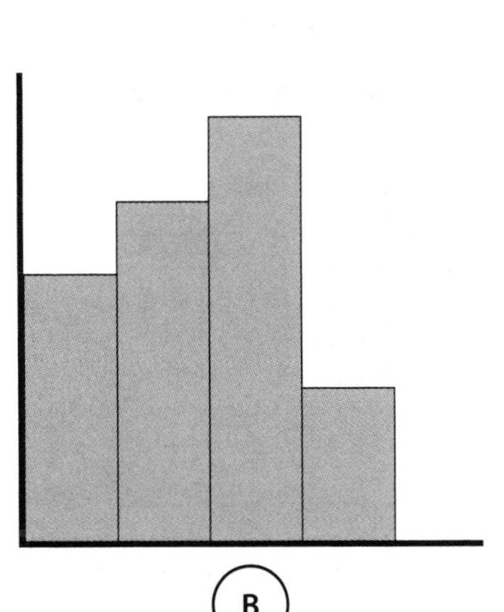

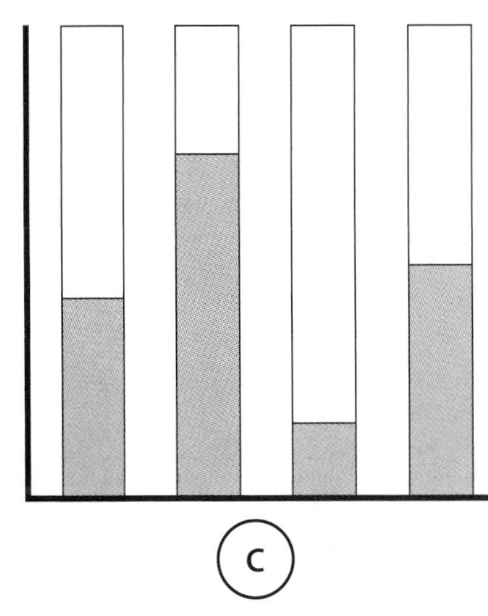

Solve.

1. Which is the strip graph? ______________ The bar graph? ____________

   The histogram? ______________

2. If you wanted to show the number of people that live in different city blocks, but wanted to distinguish between male and female, which graph would you use?

   ____

3. Which graph would you use to show the number of cars that entered the park each day of the week?

   ____

4. Which graph would you use to show the number of days each month that fell within a certain temperature scale?

   ____

5. If you wanted to show the exact number of students' math scores, which graph would you not use?

   ____

Answer Key

Collecting Information (page 4)

1. F
2. A
3. G
4. D
5. H
6. C
7. I
8. B
9. E
10. biased
11. biased
12. biased
13. unbiased

Ways to Collect Data (page 5)

1. B, C, D
2. A, B
3. C, D
4. A, B
5. C
6. A, B
7. D
8. D
9. C
10. C, D

Survey Says (page 6)

1. 12 students

2. 100 students

3. Rhonda's survey said that the majority of students wanted P.E. minutes to decrease. Mia's survey said that the majority wanted the minutes to stay the same. They got different results. This may have occurred because Mia surveyed a larger sample of people.

4. Mia's survey may be more accurate because it shows the opinion of a greater number of students.

5. The larger the sample, the more accurate the findings may be. Too small a sample may not give accurate results.

Watch Those Questions! (page 7)

1. The question does not include people who never watch TV or those who watch it more than 15 hours a week.
Possible answer: How much TV do you watch in a week?

a) 0 hours b) 1–5 hours
c) 6–10 hours d) 11–15 hours
e) 16 or more hours

2. This question is biased. People might feel that they have to answer yes.
Possible answer: More money should be raised to fund our animal shelters.

a) agree b) disagree
c) undecided

3. This question is biased toward those who like science. Possible answer: How interested are you in science?

a) extremely interested
b) somewhat interested
c) interested
d) somewhat uninterested
e) uninterested

4. This question is biased. People might feel that they have to answer yes. Possible answer: What baseball team, if any, do you support?

5. This question assumes all surveyed are under 30. Some people can fit more than one category. Possible answer: How old are you?

a) under 11 b) 11–20
c) 21–30 d) 31–40
e) over 40

Interpret a Tally Chart (page 8)

1. walk: 58 auto: 24
school bus: 19 public bus: 4
bicycle: 34 other: 2

2. walk

3. 141 students

4. 47–49 students; Since they are not old enough to drive, they must ride in an auto or a bus. Depending on what "other" includes, the number can be between 47 and 49.

5. It includes transportation that is not on the list, such as a skateboard or scooter.

6. Possible answer: Most students live close enough to the school to be able to walk; most students rely on themselves to travel to school.

Tally Ho! (page 9)

Height	Tally	Frequency
132 cm–134 cm	|||	3
135 cm–137 cm	卌 |	6
138 cm–140 cm	||||	4
141 cm–143 cm	卌 |	6
144 cm–146 cm	卌 卌	10
147 cm–149 cm	卌 卌 |	11
150 cm–152 cm	卌 ||	7
153 cm–155 cm	|||	3
156 cm–158 cm	||||	4

1. 147 cm–149 cm

2. 132 cm–134 cm and 153 cm–155 cm

3. 54 students

4. 150 cm–152 cm

5. 25 students

6. Answers will vary. Possible answer: Most fifth graders are between 141 cm and 152 cm; the lower and higher the height range, the fewer the students.

Read a Pictograph (page 10)

1. 5,500 cans

2. 11,250 cans

3. 8,500 cans

4. 57,250 cans

5. July and August

6. Possible answer: People drink more beverages and, therefore, recycle more cans in the summer months.

Picture This (page 11)

1.

Tree Species	Number of Trees 🌲 = 100,000 trees
Douglas fir	🌲🌲🌲🌲🌲🌲🌲
Noble fir	🌲🌲🌲🌲
Scotch pine	🌲🌲🌲🌲🌲🌲🌲🌲🌲🌲🌲🌲🌲🌲🌲🌲🌲🌲🌲🌲
Fraser fir	🌲🌲🌲
Blue spruce	🌲🌲🌲🌲🌲🌲
White spruce	🌲🌲🌲🌲 (half tree)
Other	🌲🌲🌲🌲🌲 (half tree)

2. 5 million or 5,000,000

3. 6%

4. 1,300,000 more

5. one and a half trees

6. Possible answers: Scotch Pines grow the best in Michigan; more people want a Scotch Pine for a Christmas tree than any other.

Read a Table (page 12)

1. Pattern; Multicolored; Clear

2. Blinking; Solid; Fade in-out

3. 14

4. Clear

5. Solid, Clear

Temperature Table (page 13)

1. 3.10 inches

2. June 1988

3. High – 58.7; Low – 41.7

4. Possible answer: Variations were extreme and many records were set in both low and high temperatures. The spring of 1986 was very hot compared to the average.

Raising the Table (page 14)

1. $2.20

2. 5

3.

Items	Price	Start Item Count	End Item Count	Items Sold	Total Amount
Cookies	$.10	24	2	22	**$2.20**
Brownies	$.20	**24**	0	**24**	$4.80
Lemonade	$.25	50 cups	22 cups	**28**	**$7.00**
Water Bottles	$.75	48	28	**20**	**$15.00**
Pencils	$.15	50	**5**	45	$6.75
Artwork	$2.00	15	10	**5**	**$10.00**
				Grand Total:	**$45.75**

4. $45.75

Election Results (page 15)

1.–4. Election Results

Candidate	1st Grade	2nd Grade	3rd Grade	4th Grade	5th Grade	6th Grade	Total Votes
John	14	21	7	5	2	0	49
Chuck	20	10	15	8	5	3	61
Aleesha	3	12	23	18	25	21	102
Helen	17	2	2	1	1	0	23
Jose	5	6	9	17	18	28	83

5. Answers will vary. Possible answers include: Aleesha received the most votes in grades 2 through 6, or she was well liked at the school.

Read a Bar Graph (page 16)

1. 40 gloves
2. 10 backpacks
3. 30 to 10
4. Answers will vary. Possible answers include: Sweaters because it has the highest bar.
5. sweaters
6. 10

Fill It In (page 17)

1. When counting how many in a bar graph you start at 0 or 1 and add up.
2. 5 students; 4 students
3. 3
4. 2 birthdays
5. July, August, and November

Vertical or Horizontal? (page 18)

1. the numbers 10 to 50; or, the number of students
2. the numbers 10 to 50; or, the number of students
3. Answers will vary. Possible answers include: On the vertical graph the bars go up and on the horizontal graph the bars go across. They are similar because they provide the same information.
4. 20 students; 20 students
5. C

Make Your Own (page 19)

1.–3. Favorite Ice Cream Flavors

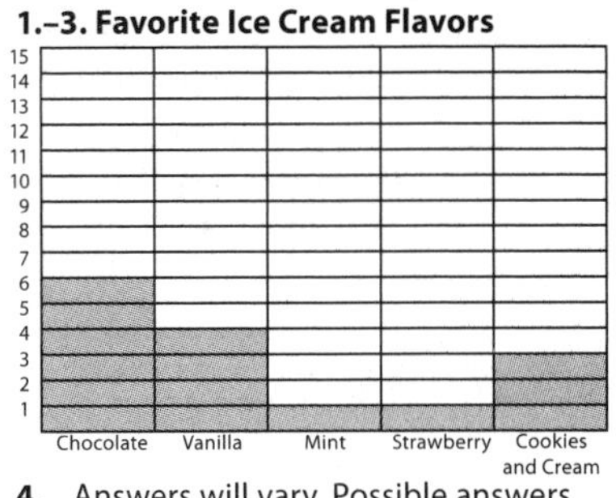

4. Answers will vary. Possible answers include: How many more people liked chocolate over vanilla? What were the least popular flavors? How many people liked vanilla over mint?

Same Info Three Ways (page 20)

1. bar graph; table graph, pictograph
2. bar graph or graph 1
3. 2 students
4. table graph or graph 2
5. Yes. The amounts for grades 5 and 6 equal 10.
6. water park

Read a Line Graph (page 21)

1. where the vertical and horizontal lines meet; the beginning of the line
2. 60 miles
3. 5 hours
4. approx. 3 ½ hours
5. 2 hours

Line It Up (page 22)

1. 200 students
2.

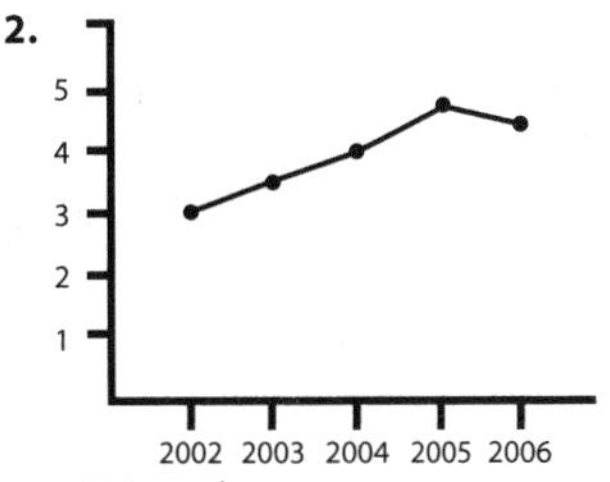

3. 450 students
4. 50%
5. 2006

Bar Graph or Line? (page 23)

1. One is a bar graph and one is a line graph. The bar graph shows rainfall for Jan.–May 2006. The line graph shows the average rainfall from Jan.–May 1961–1990.
2. 6.57 to 3.58
3. May; Jan.
4. May
5. March

Read a Pie Chart (page 24)

1. 50%; 50%
2. 25%; yes
3. 5
4. 50%
5. 16.$\overline{6}$%
6. Graph 1

A Circle Graph (page 25)

1. – 3.

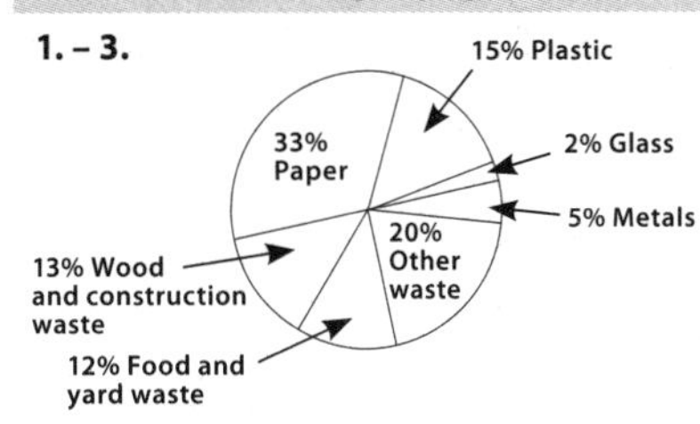

4. paper; glass
5. It is a category for those things that do not fit in the other groups. Cloth might go in this group.

Recycle Circle Graph (page 26)

1. Answers will vary. Possible answers include: Recycle Results
2. 100%; Answers will vary. Possible answers include: A circle graph represents 100%.
3.

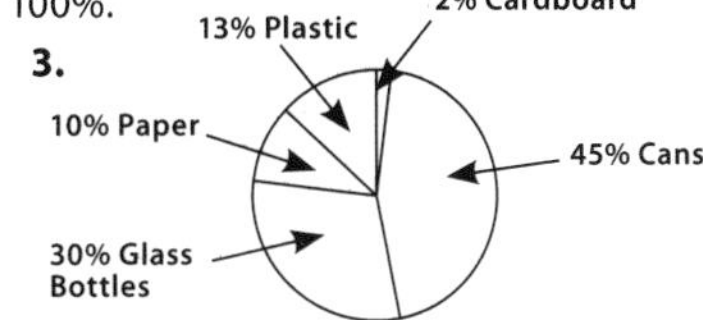

4. 15%
5. Answers will vary. Possible answers include: Cans are recycled more and cardboard is recycled less.

Circle—Line—Bar Ranch (page 27)

1. cows
2. 60%
3. 60
4. bar and line graphs
5. circle graph
6. line graph

Read a Strip Graph (page 28)

1. Intermediate Voice
2. The beginning class has almost the same number of boys and girls, but the intermediate class is mostly boys.
3. History of Music and Intermediate Voice
4. Music Theory, Beginning Percussion, Intermediate Percussion
5. Beginning Voice
6. Answers will vary. Possible answers include: Fewer females go on to take the intermediate instrument classes; males and females are equally interested in beginning music classes; more females than males are interested in music history.

A 100% Response (page 29)

1.

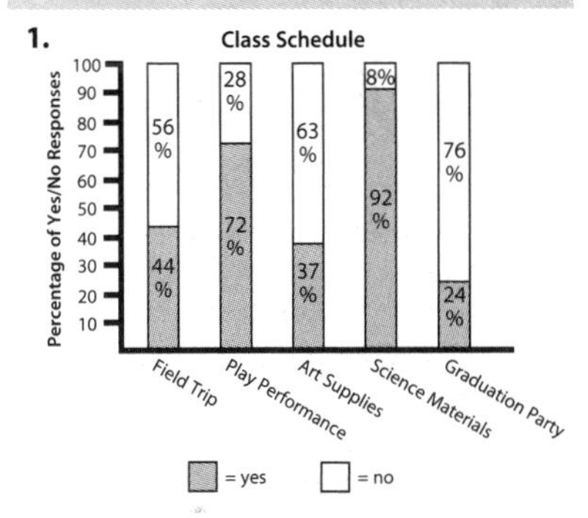

2. science materials, play performance, and field trip
3. They felt more strongly about the graduation party. The yes and no votes were about evenly split for the field trip. A greater number of students did not want to spend money on the graduation party.
4. 35% more students favored the play
5. science materials
6. Answers will vary. Possible answers include: Science is very important to this group of students; these students like drama and like to perform; perhaps the field trip is not a very exciting one.

Conduct a Survey (page 30)

Answers will vary. All responses need to total 100% for each strip on the graph.

Choose the Best One (page 31)

1. Kitchen and Bath; 11%
2. Sporting Goods
3. Shoes Department; 19%
4. 20%
5. 13 people; 16 people

6. Answers will vary. Possible answers include: More experienced people are needed to sell sporting goods and kitchen and bath products; people with no sales experience apply for jobs selling toys; the Sporting Goods Department needed a lot of new salespeople.

Read a Line Plot (page 32)

1. 10–45
2. 17, 20, 22, 36
3. 10, 40, 45; They are the oldest and youngest players.
4. There is a cluster from 15–25 and another cluster from 34-37. Answers will vary. Possible answers include: These may represent the ages of kids who are there to play after school and maybe people who have taken time off from work.
5. 10–15, 25–34, 40–45
6. 25
7. The oldest was 45; the youngest was 10.

Plot a Spot (page 33)

1.

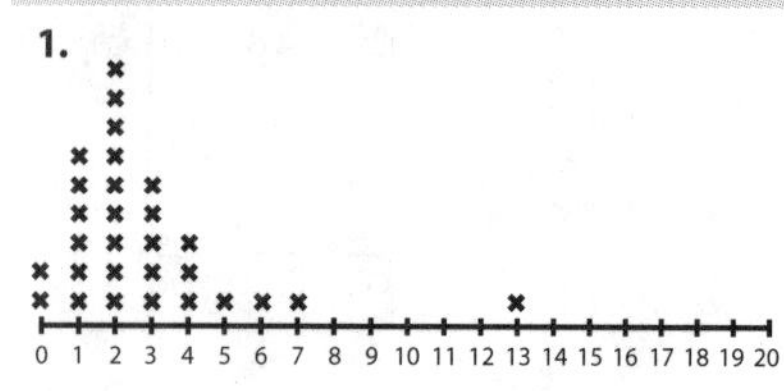

2. 13 is the outlier; It is unusual to have this many pets. Maybe one student has a lot of fish.
3. Yes; They occur between 7 and 13.
4. Yes; Clusters appear from 0 to 4.
5. 2.8 pets per person
6. 2.5 pets per person. Tossing out the outlier dropped the average a bit.

Choose the Right One (page 34)

1. 2005
2. Answers will vary. Possible answers include: increase; The last two years have shown an increase.
3. 16% larger
4. approx. 125,000
5. Population, because there would be more people in the city, and Age of Population, because there would be an increase in the 0–16 group and that would affect the other percentages.

Find an Average (page 35)

1. 30 cows; 10 cows per acre
2. 21.4 degrees
3. 14.5
4. $10.57

An Average Trip (page 36)

1. 83.0 degrees; 1999
2. July 2003; Jan 2001
3. 93 (93.08) degrees
4. Dec. 47.76; Jan. 48.6; Feb. 50.72; December
5. Answers will vary. Students should justify the time of year they choose.

Mean, Median, and Average (page 37)

1. 11 (10.65) years old
2. 11 years old
3. 17
4. 53 (52.6) points per game

Mean, Median, Mode, and Range (page 38)

1. 11
2. sandals and slip-ons
3. mean: 16 (15.86); median: 16; mode: 21; range: 12
4. 11

Read a Stem-and-Leaf Plot (page 39)

1. 30 players
2. 20–29 points
3. 8 points and 60 points
4. 52 points
5. mean = 28, median = 26, mode = 24
6. Answers will vary. Possible answers include: Most players will have between 10 and 29 points.

Put Leaves on the Stem (page 40)

1.

Stem	Leaves
5	0 1 1 4
4	0 0 5 6 7 8 9
3	0 1 1 2 2 3 4 4 5 6 7 7
2	2 3 6 6 8
1	0 1 3 3 3 5 8
0	4

2. 36 students
3. 54 and 4; 4 is an outlier because there is a gap of 6 laps between it and the next number.
4. 50
5. mean = 31.8, or 32, laps, median = 32.5, mode = 13
6. Answers will vary. Possible answers include: One third of the students ran between 30 and 39 laps.

Read a Box Plot (page 41)

1. C, B, D, E, A
2. 17
3. 8
4. 32
5. 12 and 21

Make a Box Plot (page 42)

1. 37, 43, 44, 44, 45, 45, 46, 46, 48, 52, 52, 53, 54, 56, 60; median is 46.
2. high extreme: 60; low extreme: 37; range: 23
3. 44; 53
4. 53 – 44 = 9
5.

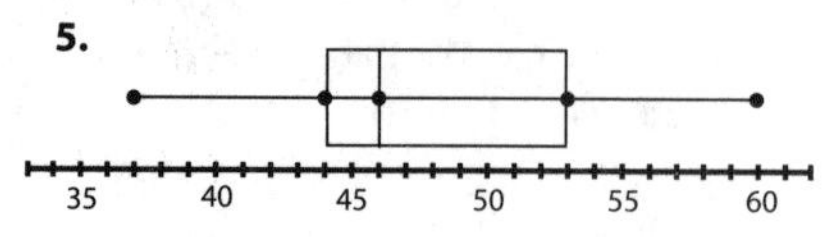

Yes, the halves of the box are not equal.
6. Answers will vary. Possible answers include: During April, most temperatures will fall between 44 and 53 degrees.

Read a Histogram (page 43)

1. 10 students; Histogram A
2. 15 students; either histogram
3. They both tell how many students scored within a certain range, they both give math score ranges. Histogram A has a smaller range of scores. Histogram B has a larger range of scores. The totals for each range show up differently. Histogram B makes it look like more students did well on the test.
4. Histogram A is more useful because it tells more precisely how many students scored by using a narrower range.
5. You could first determine the appropiate number of categories, with one category that starts with the passing score.

Same Story, Different Plots (page 44)

1. median = 84
2. 80–89 and 79–87
3. 100 – 65 = 35 and 100 – 64 = 36
4. yes; 64 and 100
5. the histogram; if a passing score is 70, I can tell how many students scored above that.
6. Answers will vary. Possible answers include: Most students scored between 70 and 89; 64 and 100 are unusual scores for this test.

The Best Choice (page 45)

1. C, A, B
2. C
3. A
4. B
5. B